All this ROAR-SOME fun inside...

JURASSIC EXPLORERS
PRESENTS

WORLD OF DINOSAURS

THIS BOOK BELONGS TO

_____

_____

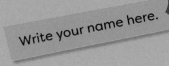
Write your name here.

LittleBrother BOOKS

Published 2021.

Little Brother Books Ltd, Ground Floor,
23 Southernhay East, Exeter, Devon EX1 1QL
books@littlebrotherbooks.co.uk | www.littlebrotherbooks.co.uk

Printed in Poland. ul. Połczyńska 99,01-303 Warszawa.

Turn the page to enter the wonderful world of dinosaurs...

AWESOME FACTS

These amazing dinosaur facts will blow your mind!

The world's first dinosaurs were all small – bigger dinos didn't come along until later.

BOOM!

Scientists used to think that all dinosaurs had scales but they now know that lots of them were covered in feathers.

Dinosaurs are usually named after the person who found them, the place they were found or after their features.

Sharks existed before dinosaurs.

AMAZING!

Everything we know about most dinosaurs comes from a single tooth or fossil.

MIND-BLOWING!

All dinosaurs had tails to help them balance and claws for fighting or gathering food.

When dinosaurs first existed, the Earth's land was all connected as one huge continent called Pangaea.

New dinosaurs are still being discovered today.

COOL!

Scientists believe that a massive meteorite hit the Earth 66 million years ago causing dinosaurs to die out.

Dinosaurs ruled the land but they couldn't swim or fly.

ALL ABOUT...
TYRANNOSAURUS

Meet T-Rex, the ferocious dinosaur king!

FOSSIL FUN

Which Tyrannosaurus fossil is the odd one out?

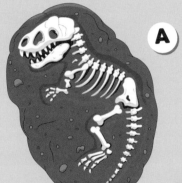

A

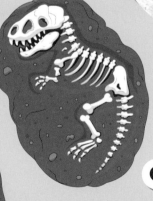

B

C

IT'S A FACT!
Tyrannosaurus could swallow small dinosaurs in one gulp.

DID YOU KNOW?
Tyrannosaurus was a fast runner. Only super quick dinos stood a chance of escaping this speedy beast.

Dino Report

NAME: TYRANNOSAURUS (TYE-RAN-OH-SORE-US) **MEANING:** TYRANT LIZARD **FOOD:** MEAT **SIZE:** 12M

WOW!
A Tyrannosaurus's powerful bite could crush bones.

Huge brain.

Mighty jaws packed with sharp teeth.

It walked on two legs.

Tiny arms which were almost useless.

Answers on pages 76-77.

HURRY HOME

Quick! The eggs are hatching!

Can you guide this T-Rex back to its nest before the rest of its babies appear?

START

10

Tick a circle as you pass each one.

FINISH

Answers on pages 76-77.

TWO MINUTE CHALLENGE

Can you complete these dino activities in two minutes or less?

READY, STEADY, GO!

Colour 5 leaves green, 3 leaves red and 2 leaves yellow.

Draw 8 dinosaur eggs in the nest.

Count the footprint fossils in this Jurassic jumble.

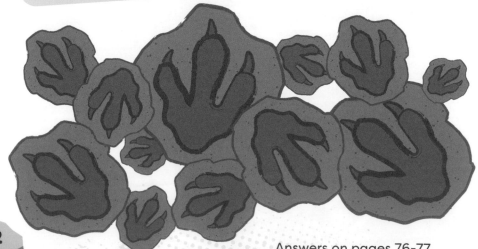

Colour the stop watch if you smashed the two minute challenge.

12

Answers on pages 76-77.

CRACK THE CODE

Giganotosaurus was one of the world's largest dinosaurs. Use the key below to uncover some more facts about this prehistoric giant.

KEY

A	B	C	D	E	F	G	H	I	J	K	L	M

N	O	P	Q	R	S	T	U	V	W	X	Y	Z

1 Giganotosaurus means

___ ___ ___ ___ ___

southern lizard.

2 Giganotosaurus had a good sense of

___ ___ ___ ___ ___

3 Giganotosaurus had a

___ ___ ___ ___ ___

body.

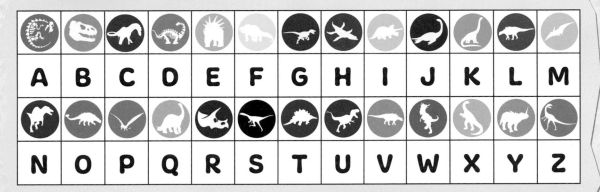

Answers on pages 76-77.

TRICERATOPS

Introducing the biggest of the horned dinosaurs.

TRICERATOPS TRAILS

Which trail will lead the Triceratops to its leafy lunch?

A   B   C

Bulky body.

Dino Report

NAME: TRICERATOPS (TRI-SERRA-TOPS)   **MEANING:** THREE-HORNED FACE   **FOOD:** PLANTS   **SIZE:** 9M

Bony frill to protect its neck.

IT'S A FACT!
Triceratops used its large neck frill like a shield.

Sharp horns for fighting or fending off attackers.

WOW!
Triceratops had a whopping 800 teeth.

Beak-like mouth to nip plants.

DID YOU KNOW?
Hefty Triceratops was as big as an elephant and too heavy to walk quickly.

Answers on pages 76-77.

15

MOVEABLE DINO

Make your very own dinosaur for a prehistoric playtime. It can even move its head, tail and legs!

YOU WILL NEED

Thin cardboard

Split pins

Glue   Scissors

HOW TO MAKE

1. Cut out the page opposite and glue it onto thin card.

2. Carefully cut out the dinosaur pieces.

3. Use split pins to attach the head, tail and legs onto the dinosaur's body where shown by the crosses.

4. Your prehistoric pal is now ready to play!

Adult guidance is needed for this activity.

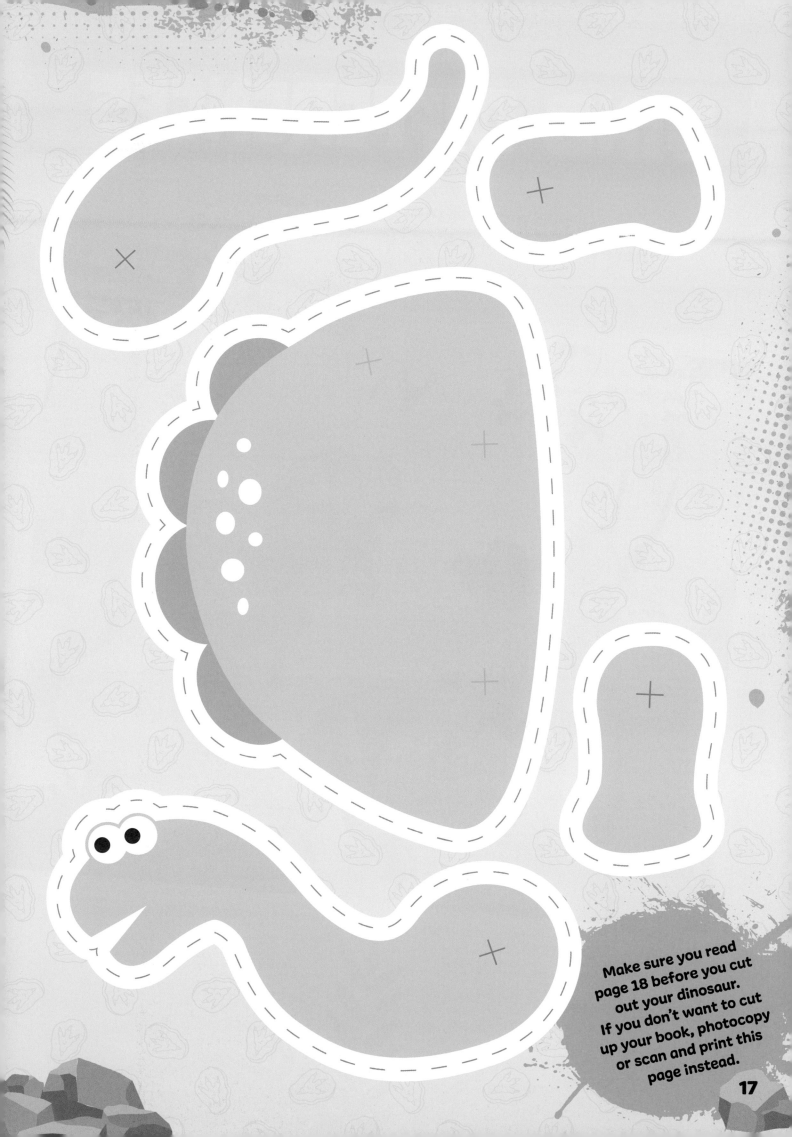

Make sure you read page 18 before you cut out your dinosaur. If you don't want to cut up your book, photocopy or scan and print this page instead.

17

DINO DIFFERENCES

These two pictures may look the same but there are eight sneaky differences in picture B.

A

18

B

Colour a dinosaur egg each time you spot a difference.

Answers on pages 76-77.

BIG AND SMALL

Just look at the size of some of these dinosaur body parts compared to everyday objects!

EYE EYE

The mighty T-Rex had eyeballs as big as clenched fists! Wow!

SMALL BRAIN

Although Stegosaurus was massive, it had a tiny brain that was only about the size of an apple.

TINY DINO

Not all dinosaurs were giants. The mini Microraptor was only about the size of a seagull.

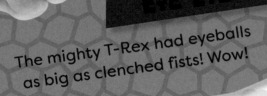

BUMPER TO BUMPER

Ankylosaurus might have been built like a tank but it was as long as two cars. Vroom vroom!

GIANT EGGS

The almighty Apatosaurus laid supersized eggs. Each one was as big as a basketball.

SUPER LONG

With its loooong neck and tail, the enormous Diplodocus was the same length as a blue whale.

ALL ABOUT...
VELOCIRAPTOR

This feathered dinosaur was small but vicious.

> Long tail for balance when running.

EGG COUNT

How many Velociraptor eggs can you count in this jumble?

There are _____ eggs.

IT'S A FACT!
Velociraptor was only the size of a large dog.

Dino Report

NAME: VELOCIRAPTOR (VEL-OSS-EE-RAP-TOR) **MEANING:** SPEED THIEF **FOOD:** MEAT **SIZE:** 2M

NEXT PLEASE!

These dinosaurs are lining up neatly! Can you work out which one comes next in each row?

1

?

2

?

3

?

4

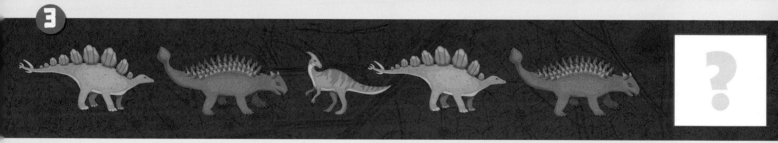

?

COLOUR IT!

Follow the footprints to the Stegosaurus then colour it in.

Answers on pages 76-77.

DOTTY DIPPY

Finish this picture by joining the dots, then add some cool colours to the Diplodocus.

Trace over the leaves for the dinosaur's dinner.

BATTLE TIME

DID YOU KNOW?
A Giganotosaurus's biggest teeth were 20cm long.

Excellent eye sight.

Great sense of smell.

Solid, bulky body.

Long, blade-like teeth.

DID YOU KNOW?
Giganotosaurus was as heavy as 125 fully grown people.

Giganotosaurus Scores	
Size	/10
Strength	/10
Speed	/10
Fierceness	/10
TOTAL	/40

GIGANOTOSAURUS

NAME: GIGANOTOSAURUS (GIG-AN-OH-TOE-SORE-US) **MEANING:** GIANT SOUTHERN LIZARD **FOOD:** MEAT **SIZE:** 12M

Sharp, dagger-like teeth.

Who would win in a fight between these two fierce predators? Choose ratings for each dinosaur and fill out their score sheets. The one with the highest total score is the champion.

Large body.

DID YOU KNOW?
Even a baby Mapusaurus could tear meat from a dead dinosaur.

Clawed fingers for grasping prey.

Strong back legs.

DID YOU KNOW?
Mapusaurus is only known from incomplete skeletons so it may have been even longer than scientists estimate.

Mapusaurus Scores	
Size	/10
Strength	/10
Speed	/10
Fierceness	/10
TOTAL	/40

VS MAPUSAURUS

NAME: MAPUSAURUS (MAH-PUH-SORE-US) **MEANING:** EARTH LIZARD **FOOD:** MEAT **SIZE:** 13M

THE WINNER IS ....

ALL ABOUT...

STEGOSAURUS

Introducing the biggest of the horned dinosaurs.

Spiked tail to fend off attackers.

WOW!
Fossils of an Allosaurus with holes made by a Stegosaurus's spiked tail have been found.

IT'S A FACT!
Stegosaurus could swing its tail from side to side. The spike on the end would have made it a deadly weapon.

Elephant-sized body.

Dino Report

NAME: STEGOSAURUS (STEG-OH-SORE-US) **MEANING:** ROOF LIZARD **FOOD:** PLANTS **SIZE:** 9M

UP CLOSE

Which of these close-ups doesn't belong to the Stegosaurus?

A

B

C

Two rows of bony back plates.

Toothless beak.

DID YOU KNOW?
Some scientists believe that a Stegosaurus's back plates may have flashed red to warn off attackers.

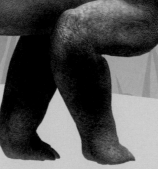

Answers on pages 76-77.

STEGOSAURUS
SKELETON

YOU WILL NEED

Thin cardboard

Dried pasta in lots of different shapes

PVA glue

A glue spreader

This brilliant Stegosaurus skeleton is made out of pasta pieces. Who knew fusilli could be so much fun!

HOW TO MAKE

1 On a piece of card, arrange pieces of pasta in a curved shape to make the dinosaur's neck, back and tail. Glue the pasta pieces to the card.

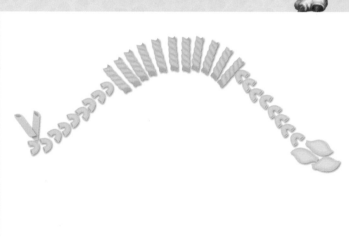

2 Arrange more pieces of pasta to make the dinosaur's back plates and tummy. Glue these pieces to the card.

3 Finally, glue on pieces of pasta to make the dinosaur's legs.

4 Allow the glue to dry completely before you pick your picture up.

GET CREATIVE!

Want to make some more pasta skeletons? Then use these simple pictures as inspiration.

SPOT IT!

Can you find this fossil hidden somewhere on these pages?

DISCOVERY REPORT

Wow, you've just found a new dinosaur!
Fill in this report to tell the world about
your amazing discovery.

My dinosaur is called _____

It is _____ million years old

It is as big as a

It is as heavy as a

It likes to eat

The words that best describe my dinosaur are

Friendly ☑ Scary ☑

Fierce ☑ Fast ☑

Strong ☑ Slow ☐

Draw a picture of your dinosaur here.

PARASAUROLOPHUS

Introducing the musical dinosaur!

Strong back legs.

DID YOU KNOW?
The Parasaurolophus's fancy head crest could make a sound like a trumpet. This may have been how they talked to other dinosaurs.

Dino Report

NAME: PARASAUROLOPHUS (PA-RA-SAW-ROL-OFF-US) **MEANING:** NEAR CRESTED LIZARD **FOOD:** PLANTS **SIZE:** 9M

Answers on pages 76-77.

FIND THE FRIENDS

This Parasaurolophus has been separated from its herd. Can you follow the trail to lead it back to its friends?

START

Trace the trail with a pencil and complete the activities along the way.

1 Jump on the stones to cross the water.

2 Parasaurolophus is using its crest to call to its friends. Circle the sound it makes.

3 Find the hidden fossil.

4 Colour the leaves for lunch.

5 Count the footsteps back to the herd.

FINISH

37

FANTASTIC FOSSILS

Everything we know about dinosaurs comes from the fossils they left behind. Read on to find out more about these clues from the past.

WHAT IS A FOSSIL?

Fossils are the remains of animals or plants that died a long time ago that have been preserved in the Earth. They are formed over millions of years and are very rare.

SPOT IT!

Can you spot this footprint fossil hidden somewhere on these pages?

DID YOU KNOW?

Some dinosaur fossils were formed when the remains of the dinosaur faded away leaving a mould of its body in rock or mud.

HOW FOSSILS ARE MADE

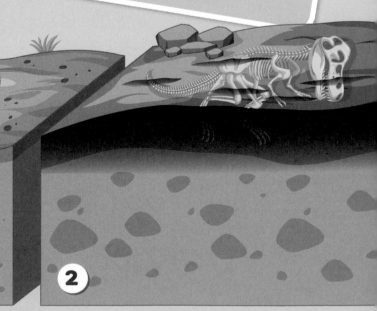

1 A dinosaur dies and its body is buried under mud.

2 After a few years, only the dinosaur's bones remain.

MEET DIPPY

Sometimes the fossils you see in museums are models of the original fossil so that the real one can be kept safe in storage. A model of a Diplodocus skeleton, called Dippy, was displayed at the Natural History Museum in London for over 100 years.

FIRST FINDS

In 1677, Robert Plot found a huge fossil bone that he couldn't identify as coming from any animal known at that time. In the 1800s, big tooth fossils and skeletons were discovered by Gideon and Mary Ann Mantell. But it wasn't until 1842 that scientist Sir Richard Owen realised these fossils all belonged to a group of extinct animals. He named them dinosaurs which means terrible lizards.

IT'S A FACT!
Dinosaur fossils have been found all over the world.

DID YOU KNOW?
Before dinosaur fossils were discovered, people had no idea that dinosaurs had ever existed.

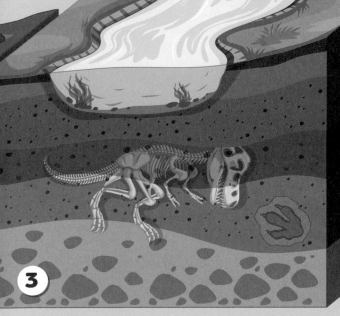

3

Over millions of years, the Earth changes and the sea spreads over the buried dinosaur. Slowly its bones turn into stone.

4

The Earth continues to change until the sea disappears and the ground above the dinosaur wears away. Now the fossil is ready to be discovered!

ALL ABOUT...
SPINOSAURUS

GETTING BIGGER

Meet the enormous dinosaur with the impressive sail.

Can you put these fierce Spinosaurus dinos in order of size, starting with the smallest?

A

B

C

IT'S A FACT!
Spinosaurus dined on fish which it caught in shallow waters. Its webbed feet were perfectly designed for walking along riverbeds.

Dino Report

NAME: SPINOSAURUS (SPINE-OH-SORE-US)   **MEANING:** THORN LIZARD   **FOOD:** FISH   **SIZE:** 16M

WOW!
Super-sized Spinosaurus was the biggest meat-eating dinosaur.

High nostrils for breathing in water.

Eye-catching sail.

Crocodile-like teeth.

Webbed feet.

DID YOU KNOW?
Scientists don't really know what the Spinosaurus sail was for. It might have helped the dinosaur stay underwater or been used to store energy.

Answers on pages 76-77.

DINO ALERT!

Can you match these stomping dinos to their shadows? Which one doesn't have a shadow match?

A

B

C

D

COUNT IT!

How many footprint fossils are hidden on these pages?

43

DANGEROUS DINOS

Rate these prehistoric predators from **1 to 10** to decide which is the most fierce dinosaur of all!

COELOPHYSIS
(SEEL-OH-FIE-SIS)

RATING

A fast and fierce hunter that grasped its prey in its deadly claws.

SPINOSAURUS
(SPINE-OH-SORE-US)

RATING

The biggest meat-eater was huge with sharp teeth.

CARCHARODONTOSAURUS
(CAR-CARE-OH-DON-TOE-SORE-US)

This giant predator with shark-like teeth was not to be messed with!

RATING

TYRANNOSAURUS
(TYE-RAN-OH-SORE-US)

RATING

The dinosaur king was a deadly predator with a mighty bite.

LEAST FIERCE

》》 1 》》 2 》》 3 》》 4 》》 5

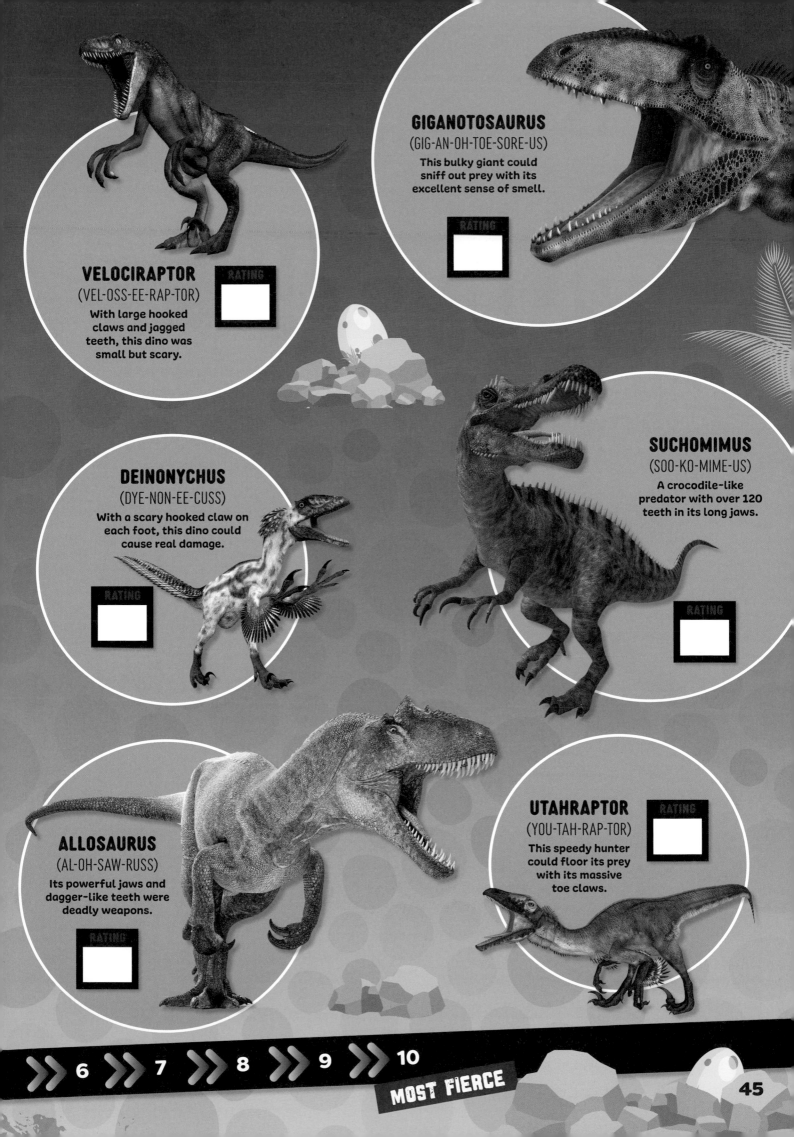

GIGANOTOSAURUS
(GIG-AN-OH-TOE-SORE-US)

This bulky giant could sniff out prey with its excellent sense of smell.

RATING

VELOCIRAPTOR
(VEL-OSS-EE-RAP-TOR)

RATING

With large hooked claws and jagged teeth, this dino was small but scary.

DEINONYCHUS
(DYE-NON-EE-CUSS)

With a scary hooked claw on each foot, this dino could cause real damage.

RATING

SUCHOMIMUS
(SOO-KO-MIME-US)

A crocodile-like predator with over 120 teeth in its long jaws.

RATING

ALLOSAURUS
(AL-OH-SAW-RUSS)

Its powerful jaws and dagger-like teeth were deadly weapons.

RATING

UTAHRAPTOR
(YOU-TAH-RAP-TOR)

RATING

This speedy hunter could floor its prey with its massive toe claws.

6   7   8   9   10

MOST FIERCE

Thin, pointy teeth.

Small head for such a big body.

ALL ABOUT...
DIPLODOCUS

This gigantic beast was one of the longest dinosaurs.

DINO COLOURS

Use your favourite pens or pencils to colour this HUGE Diplodocus.

Dino Report

NAME: DIPLODOCUS (DIP-LOW DOCK-US) **MEANING:** DOUBLE BEAM **FOOD:** PLANTS **SIZE:** 27M

IT'S A FACT!
Diplodocus was a plant-eating dino. It swallowed stones to help digest the food inside its enormous stomach.

WOW!
Diplodocus used it's long tail like a whip to scare of predators. It made a loud booming sound.

Long neck.

Long tail for scaring off predators.

DID YOU KNOW?
Some scientists think that Diplodocus wouldn't have been able to hold its long neck up high because its heart couldn't have pumped blood that far upwards.

MAKE A MASK

This colourful dinosaur mask is easy to make and fun to wear!

YOU WILL NEED

Paper plate

Thin card

Paper straw

Red paint
Green paint

Sticky tape

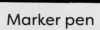
Marker pen

Paintbrush

Scissors   Glue

HOW TO MAKE

1 Paint the underside of the paper plate green and leave it to dry.

2 Paint the thin card red. Once it's dry, cut out nine red triangle shapes.

3 Glue eight of the red triangles around the edge of the paper plate and the remaining one in the middle.

4

Cut out eye holes then use a marker pen to draw on a nose and mouth.

Adult guidance is needed for this activity.

5

Attach a paper straw to the back of one side of your mask using sticky tape – this is so you can hold it in front of your face.

6

Hold the mask up to your face and practise your dinosaur

ROAR!

WHO AM I?

It's time to become a dino detective! Read the clues below and work out which dinosaurs are being described.

DIPLODOCUS

PARASAUROLOPHUS

DINO A
I walked on four legs.
I had a neck frill.
I had three horns.

DINO B
I was very big.
I had a spike on the end of my tail.
I had back plates.

I AM _____

I AM _____

STEGOSAURUS

TRICERATOPS

DINO C

I was one of the biggest dinosaurs.
My back legs were longer
than my front.
I had a long neck.

DINO D

I could stand on my back legs.
I had a pointed tail.
I had a crest on my head.

I AM _____

I AM _____

DINOSAUR DINNERS

Read on to find out what was on the menu for dinosaurs with rumbling tummies!

MEAT-EATERS

Dinosaurs that ate meat, like the Spinosaurus, were carnivores. They were usually brilliant hunters with powerful jaws and sharp teeth. These deadly predators often had good eyesight for spotting their prey, strong legs for running quickly and thick tails to help them balance on the move.

Draw a delicious dinner for a hungry meat-eater.

Carnivore Menu

Other dinosaurs
Small mammals
Reptiles
Insects
Fish

PLANT-EATERS

Dinosaurs that ate plants, like the Diplodocus, were herbivores. Most of them had strong mouths for gripping branches and flat teeth which were good for chewing. Some had long necks to reach high up leaves or beak-like mouths which were helpful for snipping plants.

Draw a yummy lunch perfect for a plant-eater.

Herbivore Menu

Leaves
Moss
Seeds
Fruit
Berries

ALL ABOUT...

ALLOSAURUS

This speedy dino was a fierce hunter.

IT'S A FACT!

Allosaurus had strong claws on its three-fingered hands. It used its powerful grip to cling onto its prey.

Long tail for balance.

Powerful legs for running quickly.

Dino Report

NAME: ALLOSAURUS (AL-OH-SAW-RUSS)   **MEANING:** OTHER LIZARD   **FOOD:** MEAT   **SIZE:** 12M

70 sharp teeth.

FIERCE FACT

What did Allosaurus use to slash at its prey? Copy the letters into the matching coloured circles to reveal the answer.

◯ ◯ ◯ ◯ ◯

H E T E T

WOW!
In the Jurassic period, Allosaurus was the king of the North American predators.

Razor sharp claws.

Answers on pages 76-77.

STARLIT SEARCH

Can you spot all of the small images in the big picture before it gets too dark to see?

Tick a circle as you spot each one.

57

HANDPRINT FUN

This one-of-a-kind dinosaur picture is super quick to make and the right amount of messy too!

Make sure you read page 60 before you cut out the opposite page. If you don't want to cut up your book, photocopy or scan and print page 59 instead.

YOU WILL NEED

Scissors   Glue

Green paint

Paintbrush

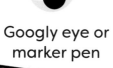

Googly eye or marker pen

HOW TO MAKE

1 Ask an adult to cut out the opposite page.

2 Use a paintbrush to cover one of your hands in green paint, then make an upside down handprint at the bottom of the cut-out page.

3 Paint a green dinosaur neck and head joining on to the top of your handprint.

4 Once the paint is completely dry, stick on a googly eye or draw on an eye with a marker pen.

5 Proudly display your one-of-a-kind dino art!

Adult guidance is needed for this activity.

MICRORAPTOR

Meet the small and speedy bird-like dino.

SHADOW MATCH

Which shadow matches this picture of a gliding Microraptor?

A

B

C

Fan of feathers.

Dino Report

NAME: MICRORAPTOR (MIKE-ROW-RAP-TOR) **MEANING:** SMALL THIEF **FOOD:** MEAT **SIZE:** 40CM

WOW!
The long feathers on its arms and legs made the Microraptor a clumsy runner.

IT'S A FACT!
The tiny Microraptor ate small mammals, insects and lizards. It caught its prey with its sharp teeth and claws.

Small, pointed teeth.

Wings like a bird.

DID YOU KNOW?
Microraptor had feathered arms and legs but it couldn't fly. Instead, it glided between trees, using its long tail to keep balance.

Sharp claws.

Answers on pages 76-77.

RECORD BREAKERS

From biggest to smallest and tallest to longest, meet the dinosaurs that smashed the records!

Colour the trophy next to your favourite record breaker.

SMALLEST

At 40cm long, the tiny Microraptor was about the size of a seagull when fully grown.

TALLEST

The long-necked Sauroposeidon was a whopping 18m tall – that's about the height of a six storey building.

AMAZING!

BIGGEST MEAT-EATER

Imagine three cars parked bumper to bumper – at 16m, that's about the length of the deadly Spinosaurus.

FASTEST

Reaching speeds of up to 43mph, the Dromiceiomimus was as quick as a car.

VROOM VROOM

MOST TEETH

Lambeosaurus and other hadrosaurs had more than 1,000 teeth. Imagine having to keep all of those clean!

LONGEST TAIL

The award for longest tail goes to the Diplodocus with an impressive length of 13-14m.

WOW!

LONGEST NECK

Mamenchisaurus's 14m neck was longer than a double decker bus. That would have been handy for reaching high-up leaves!

SMALLEST BRAIN

The prize for smallest brain goes to the Stegosaurus with its apple-sized entry.

LONGEST CLAW

With 91cm claws that were about as long as a man's arm, the Therizinosaurus would have been a scary sight!

LONGEST

The Diplodocus could reach up to 53.3m - that's longer than two swimming pools!

63

FOSSIL FINDS

Scientists have discovered some new dinosaur fossils. Can you draw lines to match them into pairs?

A

B

C

D

E

F

G

I

H

J

Colour the dinosaur when you've finished.

DINOSAUR LOLs!

Roar with laughter at these funny Jurassic jokes!

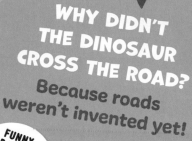

WHY DIDN'T THE DINOSAUR CROSS THE ROAD?
Because roads weren't invented yet!

FUNNY RATING /5

WHAT DOES A TYRANNOSAURUS EAT?
Anything he wants!

FUNNY RATING /5

WHAT KIND OF DINOSAUR CAN JUMP HIGHER THAN A HOUSE?
Any kind – houses can't jump!

FUNNY RATING /5

WHY DO MUSEUMS EXHIBIT OLD DINOSAUR BONES?
Because they can't afford new ones!

FUNNY RATING /5

WHY DOES DIPLODOCUS HAVE SUCH A LONG NECK?
Because its feet smell!

FUNNY RATING /5

RATE IT!

Give each joke a funny rating out of 5.

1 = The opposite of funny!
2 = A big thumbs down!
3 = It's given me the giggles!
4 = Laugh out loud funny!
5 = Completely roar-some!

WHAT DO YOU CALL A SLEEPING DINOSAUR?
A dino-snore!

FUNNY RATING /5

ALL ABOUT...
ANKYLOSAURUS

FOOTPRINT FUN

What colour Ankylosaurus footprint comes next in the sequence?

Introducing the slow-moving dino that was as tough as a tank.

DID YOU KNOW?
Ankylosaurus swallowed its food whole. The plants and leaves it feasted on were broken down inside its stomach.

Dino Report

NAME: ANKYLOSAURUS (AN-KIE-LOH-SORE-US) **MEANING:** STIFF LIZARD **FOOD:** PLANTS **SIZE:** 10M

WOW!
Ankylosaurus's bulky body was wider than it was tall.

IT'S A FACT!
The thick plates, studs and spikes covering Ankylosaurus's body acted like armour and made the tough dino hard to attack.

Bony tail club was a deadly weapon.

Covered in studs.

Wide body.

Small, leaf-shaped teeth.

Answers on pages 76-77.

HOME SWEET HOME

Dinosaurs lived in lots of different habitats around the world. Let's explore some of their homes.

DESERTS

The Velociraptor was one of the dinosaurs that lived in the scorching desert. Desert dinos ate plants that provided them with both food and water.

FORESTS

Lots of dinosaurs, including Tyrannosaurus, lived in woodlands. Some were cool, shady places and others were hot and swampy.

DID YOU KNOW?
When the first dinosaurs lived on Earth, flowers didn't exist.

BY WATER

Coastlines and riverbanks were the perfect homes for plant and fish-eaters. One of the earliest dinosaurs, the Eoraptor, lived in the river valleys of Argentina.

PLAINS

Flat plains and open scrublands were home to many dinosaurs, including Diplodocus. Plants that didn't need much water grew in these huge areas of dry land.

PLANT PUZZLE

Draw lines to match these prehistoric plants to their shadows.

1
2
3
4

A
B
C
D

PREHISTORIC
PALS

Add some fierce colours to these roar-some dinosaurs.

TYRANNOSAURUS

PARASAUROLOPHUS

TRICERATOPS

STEGOSAURUS

QUIZ TIME

Check out your dino knowledge with this fun quiz. All of the answers can be found somewhere in this book.

2 How many teeth did Triceratops have?

100

800

1 Which dinosaur is this?

Allosaurus ✓

Stegosaurus ✓

3 What are meat-eating dinosaurs called?

Herbivores ✓

Carnivores ✓

4 What was Velociraptor the size of?

A dog ✓

An elephant ✓

5 Which dinosaur was as long as a blue whale?

Diplodocus ✓

Stegosaurus ✓

6 What did Ankylosaurus have on the end of its tail?

A club ✓

Feathers ✓

7 Which was the biggest meat-eating dinosaur?

Microraptor ✓

Spinosaurus ✓

8 What could Parasaurolophus do with its head crest?

Make a sound ✓

Blow bubbles ✓

9 What were Apatosaurus eggs the same size as?

A basketball ✓

A tennis ball ✓

10 What does dinosaur mean?

Terrible lizard ✓

Big animal ✓

Answers on pages 76-77.

DINO DICTIONARY

Read on to find out the meaning of lots of dinosaur words.

ARMOUR:
Body coverings such as spikes or plates that protect an animal from harm.

CARNIVORE:
An animal that eats other animals.

CRETACEOUS:
One of the time periods that dinosaurs lived in, between 145 and 66 million years ago.

EVOLVE:
The way in which animals change and adapt over a long time to help them survive.

EXTINCT:
When a species of animal dies out.

FOSSIL:
The remains of an animal or plant that died a long time ago, preserved in the Earth.

HABITAT:
The place where an animal lives.

HERBIVORE:
An animal that eats plants.

HERD:
A group of animals that live or travel together.

COUNT IT!

How many dinosaur footprints can you count in this trail?

74

Can you put your favourite dinosaur word into a sentence?

JURASSIC:
One of the time periods that dinosaurs lived in, between 200 and 145 million years ago.

MESOZOIC ERA:
The time when dinosaurs lived, made up of the Triassic, Jurassic and Cretaceous periods.

METEORITE:
A lump of rock that falls from space to the Earth.

MUSEUM:
A place where historical artefacts are kept and displayed.

OMNIVORE:
An animal that eats both other animals and plants.

PALAEONTOLOGIST:
A scientist who studies fossils.

PREDATOR:
An animal that hunts and kills other animals for food.

PREY:
Animals that are killed and eaten by other animals.

TRIASSIC:
One of the time periods that dinosaurs lived in, between 251 and 200 million years ago.

Answers on pages 76-77.

ANSWERS

PAGES 8-9
FOSSIL FUN
B.

PAGES 10-11
HURRY HOME

PAGE 12
TWO MINUTE CHALLENGE
There are 12 footprint fossils.

PAGE 13
CRACK THE CODE
1. Giant.
2. Smell.
3. Bulky.

PAGES 14-15
TRICERATOPS TRAILS
B.

PAGES 18-19
DINO DIFFERENCES

PAGES 22-23
EGG COUNT
9.

PAGE 24
NEXT PLEASE!
1.
2.
3.
4.

PAGES 28-29
UP CLOSE
A.

PAGES 30-31
SPOT IT!

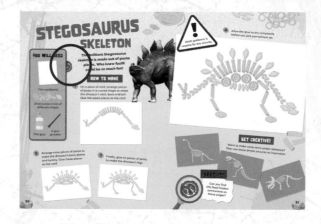

PAGES 34-35
FOSSIL FIND

76

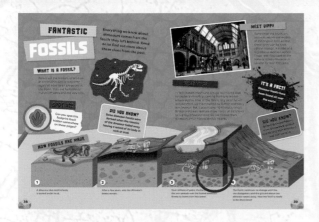